Note to parents, carers and teachers

Read it yourself is a series of modern stories, favourite characters and traditional tales written in a simple way for children who are learning to read. The books can be read independently or as part of a guided reading session.

Each book is carefully structured to include many high-frequency words vital for first reading. The sentences on each page are supported closely by pictures to help with understanding, and to offer lively details to talk about.

The books are graded into four levels that progressively introduce wider vocabulary and longer stories as a reader's ability and confidence grows.

Ideas for use

- Although your child will now be progressing towards silent, independent reading, let her know that your help and encouragement is always available.

- Developing readers can be concentrating so hard on the words that they sometimes don't fully grasp the meaning of what they're reading. Answering the puzzle questions on pages 46 and 47 will help with understanding.

For more information and advice on Read it yourself and book banding, visit www.ladybird.com/readityourself

Book Band 9

Level 4 is ideal for children who are ready to read longer stories with a wider vocabulary and are eager to start reading independently.

Special features:

Clear type

Full, exciting story

Richer, more varied vocabulary

Pod the robot was great at building things, too.

"What will we build now?" asked Sam one day.

"Can we build another robot, please?" said Pod.

8

Longer sentences

Detailed illustrations capture the imagination

Sam and Pod then built one more robot, called Chock. Chock was a robot who made yummy chocolates and he was also great at his job.

Everybody in the town wanted to eat Chock's tasty chocolates.

14

15

Educational Consultant: Geraldine Taylor
Book Banding Consultant: Kate Ruttle

A catalogue record for this book is available from the British Library

Published by Ladybird Books Ltd
80 Strand, London, WC2R 0RL
A Penguin Company

001

ISBN: 978-0-71819-475-8

Printed in Italy by G. Canale & C. S.p.A. – Borgaro T.se (TO)

Sam and
the Robots

Written by Mandy Ross
Illustrated by Lisa Hunt

Sam was good at building things.
One day he built a robot.

"I'm Pod," said the robot. "Who
are you?"

"I'm Sam," said Sam. "Pleased
to meet you."

Pod the robot liked to build things, too.

"What shall we build now?" asked Sam one day.

"Can we build another robot, please?" said Pod.

So Sam and Pod built a new robot. She was called Boots. Boots was a football robot and she was VERY good at her job. She scored goal after goal after goal.

Sam's school won the next match, and the next one. In fact, soon they had won ALL the football matches.

Sam and Pod built another new robot. He was called Dinner-Whizz. Dinner-Whizz was a robot who served school dinners. Dinner-Whizz was VERY good at his job and served tasty school dinners on plate after plate.

Sam and Pod then built one more robot, called Chock. Chock was a robot who made yummy chocolates and he was also great at his job.

Everybody in the town wanted to eat Chock's tasty chocolates.

Sam and Pod kept on building new robots and soon the town was full of busy robots all working hard.

All day long, they swept and they mopped, and they mopped and they swept. The whole town was sparkling clean. Everybody was happy as nobody else needed to work at all.

One day though, it all went wrong.
The robots had become too busy and
they couldn't stop cleaning.
"Stop!" said Sam.

But the robots just kept
on working and working.

Boots scored ten goals... through ten windows at school. CRASH! TINKLE! "Stop, Boots!" cried Sam.

But Boots kept on scoring goals through one window after another. CRASH! TINKLE!

Dinner-Whizz didn't stop serving school dinners, even though all the plates were full.
"Stop, Dinner-Whizz!" cried Sam.

But Dinner-Whizz kept on serving and soon the school was full of dinners.

Chock made all the wrong chocolates. "Please stop, Chock!" cried Sam. "Nobody wants chocolate carrots or chocolate pencils!"

But Chock would not stop. He just kept on making the wrong chocolates. Soon, the whole town was full of chocolates.

Even Pod started to go wrong.
"I know what's wrong," said Sam.
"You robots need a holiday!"
"What's a holiday?" asked Pod.
"On a holiday, you have time to rest
and have fun," said Sam.
"Yes please," said Pod. "As long as
we can work, too..."

So Sam and the robots got on a train to the seaside.
"The train is fun – as long as we can still work," said Pod.

The robots started to work. They swept and they mopped, and they mopped and they swept. Soon, the whole train was sparkling clean.

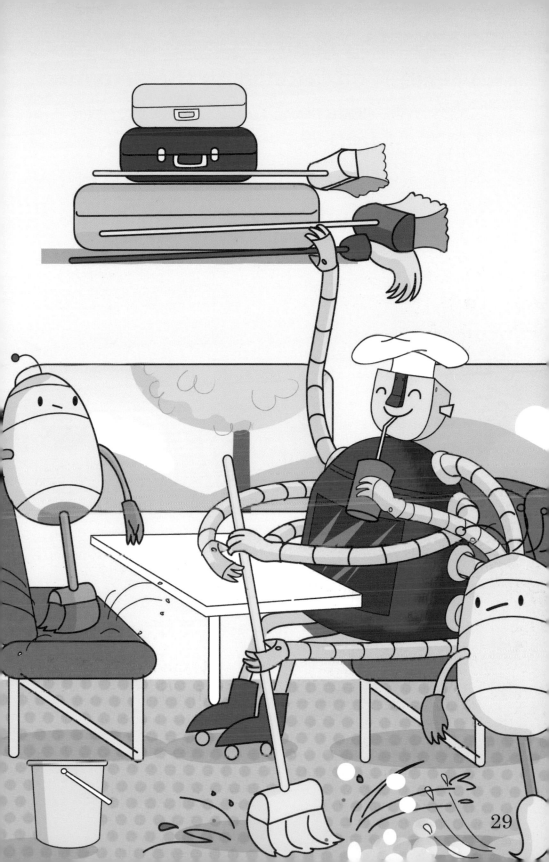

At last, the train got to the seaside.
"Now we can rest and have some
fun," said Sam.
"The seaside does look fun!" said Pod.
"All that sand needs sweeping away!
All that water needs mopping up!"

The robots started work. They swept at the sand, and they mopped up the water.

But the more they swept, the more sand there was. The more they mopped, the more water there was.

"No! Robots, please stop!" cried Sam. "You don't work on holiday! You have a rest in the sunshine, like this."

Sam lay down to have a rest. So then all the robots lay down, too.

But soon all the robots were bored.
Pod and the others got up again.
"Robots don't rest," said Pod. "We're
bored. We need to be kept busy."

Then Sam had an idea. "I know
what we need to do," he said.

Sam, Pod and all the other robots got busy. They worked hard together in the sand. They dug and they built, and they built and they dug.

Sam and the robots built a big sandcastle. They kept on building all day long and the sandcastle got bigger and bigger and bigger!

"We've built a good sandcastle!" said the robots in the end.
"No," said Sam, "you've built a GREAT sandcastle!"

Then Sam said, "Now we'll all eat
an ice cream."
"What's an ice cream?" asked Pod.
"It's a tasty, cold food," said Sam.
"No. We need cold, yummy oil,
please," says Pod.
"Yes please, cold, yummy oil,"
said all the robots.

Sam and the robots got the last
train back from the seaside.
"It was a great holiday," said Pod,
"but we will be happy to get
back home."
"And we will be VERY happy
to get back to work!" said the
other robots.

How much do you remember about the story of Sam and the Robots? Answer these questions and find out!

● What is the name of the robot Sam builds first of all?

● What is Boots the robot very good at?

● Can you remember some of the wrong chocolates Chock makes?

● Where do Sam and the robots go on holiday?

● What do the robots do there?

● What do the robots have instead of ice cream?

Unjumble these words to make words from the story, then match them to the correct pictures.

Sma Ckhco Pdo

Btsoo Dirnen-Wzihz tosorb

Read it yourself with Ladybird

Tick the books you've read!

For more confident readers who can read simple stories with help.

Level **3**

  YOU won't like this present as much as I DO!

 The Elves and the Shoemaker

☐ ☐

 Hansel and Gretel

 Harry and the Bucketful of Dinosaurs

 Jack and the Beanstalk

 Furi on Music Island

 Poppet Stows Away

 Rapunzel

 The Red Knight

☐ ☐ ☐ ☐ ☐ ☐ ☐

Longer stories for more independent, fluent readers.

Level **4**

  I am Inventing an INVENTION

 Harry and the Dinosaurs United

☐ ☐

 Heidi

 Katsuma and the Art Thief

 Luvli and the Glump-a-tron

 The Pied Piper of Hamelin

 Sam and the Robots

 Snow White and the Seven Dwarfs

 The Wizard of Oz

☐ ☐ ☐ ☐ ☐ ☐ ☐

 Available on the App Store

The Read it yourself with Ladybird app is now available for iPad, iPhone and iPod touch

App also available on Android devices